Contents

KT-377-150

quietly to Kay in the street. Kay had his *neuralyzer* in his hand.

'Listen,' began Jay. 'Must you do it? Who is she going to tell? Nobody. She works with dead people.'

Kay looked at the *neuralyzer*. 'It's not for her,' he told Jay. 'It's for me.' He looked up at the stars in the evening sky. 'They're beautiful. Do you think they're beautiful?'

'Yes, I do,' answered Jay. He understood now. Kay wanted him to use the *neuralyzer*, but not on Laurel.

Dr Weaver got out of the car and came across to the two Men in Black. 'Where are we?' she asked.

Jay did not hear her. 'I want you to help me to do this,' he said to Kay.

Kay walked across to Dr Weaver. Laurel's name was on her shirt. He put his hand across 'AUREL', and left only the 'L'. 'Elle,' he said. 'Yes?' Then he took off his dark glasses and gave them to Dr Weaver. 'Put them on,' he told her.

Jay put on his dark glasses. Elle did the same.

'I was inside a Bug,' said Kay. 'I don't want to remember that,' He gave Jay the *neuralyzer*. 'Goodbye, friend.'

Jay aimed the *neuralyzer* and fired. There was the usual light. And Kay was not a Man in Black now . . .

Chapter 12   The Woman in Black

It was some time later.

Jay walked across to the black car. Elle waited for him there. She was all in black now. She was not Laurel Weaver – she was Elle.

'Zed called,' she said to Jay. 'We have work to do.'

Jay smiled at her. 'OK,' he said.

And they climbed into the car and drove off along the streets of New York.

Men in Black

a novel by

J. J. GARDNER

based on a screen story and screenplay by
Ed Solomon

Level 2

Retold by John Escott
Series Editors: Andy Hopkins and Jocelyn Potter

Pearson Education Limited
Edinburgh Gate, Harlow,
Essex CM20 2JE, England
and Associated Companies throughout the world.

ISBN 0 582 41767 8

First published in the USA by Scholastic Inc. 1997
First published in Great Britain by Puffin Books 1997
This adaptation first published by Penguin Books 1998
Published by Addison Wesley Longman Limited and Penguin Books Ltd. 1998
New edition first published 1999

5 7 9 10 8 6

Original text and photograph copyright © Columbia Pictures Industries, Inc. 1997
Text copyright © John Escott 1998
Illustrations copyright © Chris Chaisty 1998
All rights reserved

Typeset by Digital Type, London
Set in 11/14pt Bembo
Reproduction by Anglia Graphics
Printed in Spain by Mateu Cromo, S.A. Pinto (Madrid)

Published by Pearson Education Limited in association with
Penguin Books Ltd., both companies being subsidiaries of Pearson Plc

For a complet list of titles available in the Penguin Readers series please write to your local
Pearson Education office or contact: Penguin Readers Marketing Department,
Pearson Education, Edinburgh Gate, Harlow, Essex, CM20 2JE.

Introduction

In front of them now was a small alien. And it had a human head in its hands.

   Kay smiled. 'It's Mikey!' he said. 'OK, Mikey, give me the head and put up your arms.'

Kay and Jay are Men in Black. They have a very important job. They and the other Men in Black have to find and watch all the aliens in the world.

   But now there is a Bug in New York.

'Bugs kill things – aliens and people,' said Kay. 'And we have a Bug in town . . . That's bad.'

Can Kay and Jay find the Bug before the Bug finds the Third Galaxy? The Bug wants to use the Third Galaxy to start the fighting between the Baltians and the Arquillians again. That will be very dangerous for everybody.

Men in Black is an exciting film, with Tommy Lee Jones as 'Kay', Will Smith as 'Jay' and Linda Fiorentino as the beautiful Dr Laurel Weaver. People went to see the film in more than 44 countries round the world in 1997.

   The film-makers say: 'Perhaps when you walk out of the cinema after this film, you will look at the world differently.' Perhaps when you finish reading this book, you will look at the world differently, too.

Ed Solomon wrote the story for the film *Men in Black*. He wrote the film *Bill and Ted's Excellent Adventure*, and he writes for television too. Barry Sonnenfeld made the film *Men in Black*. He also made the famous film *Shorty*, with John Travolta, and *Misery*, from a story by Stephen King. These are also Penguin Readers.

Some Words from the Story

Before you read this story, you must know the words for all the things in the picture on this page. Use a dictionary. Find the right numbers on the picture for the words below and write the numbers and words together, e.g. *1 wall*

truck screen van star belt
space ship collar galaxy wall

Chapter 1 A Small Alien

The driver stopped the van. There were lights in front of him. 'Police cars!' he thought. The men in the back of the van were Mexicans. They did not have the right papers to work in the USA, but they wanted to get good jobs, and perhaps bring their families there later. 'Stay quiet,' the driver told them in Spanish.

'Hello, Nick,' said a detective from one of the police cars. Behind him were eight other detectives. Nick knew the man. His name was Janus.

The other detectives opened the back doors of the van. After a minute, the Mexicans got out into the road.

Detective Janus looked at Nick. 'What do you get, Nick?' he said. 'A hundred dollars for each man? Two hundred?'

Then a black car came down the road. It stopped, and two men got out. They were wearing black coats, black trousers, and black shoes. 'OK,' said one of the Men in Black. 'Leave it to us, now.'

'Who are you?' asked Janus.

'We're from Station Six,' said the Man in Black.

'Is there a "Station Six"?' said Janus. 'I don't know it.'

The first Man in Black walked along the line of Mexicans. 'What do you think, Dee?' he asked the second Man in Black.

'It's difficult, Kay,' answered Dee.

Kay spoke to each Mexican in the line. 'How are you?' he asked one in Spanish. He smiled. He came to another man, and stopped smiling. 'I'm going to break your face,' he said.

The man smiled at Kay.

Kay pulled the man near to him. 'You don't understand a word of Spanish,' he said. 'Do you?'

The man smiled again but said nothing.

'This is him,' Kay said to Dee. He looked at the other men in the line. 'You can go,' he told them.

'But you can't –' began Janus.

'Shut up!' said Kay. 'We're going to have a little talk with this man. You and your men can go.'

The two Men in Black took their man away from the road and into the trees. Dee pulled out a big gun. Then Kay pulled off the man's long coat and trousers.

'We were right,' said Dee. 'This isn't a human.'

In front of them now was a small alien. And it had a human head in its hands.

Kay smiled. 'It's Mikey!' he said. 'OK, Mikey, give me the head and put up your arms.'

Mikey began to give Kay the head. Suddenly, there was a noise behind them. Kay and Dee turned round quickly. It was detective Janus. He was watching everything.

'What –?' began Janus.

Suddenly, Mikey hit the gun out of Dee's hand, and ran across to Janus.

'Kill him!' Kay told Dee. But Dee did not move. Kay used his gun. There was a noise – and suddenly Mikey was on fire.

Janus's face was white. 'Th – that wasn't –' he began.

'It wasn't human, I know,' said Kay.

The other detectives ran across to them.

'Everything is OK, everybody,' said Kay. He took something small from his coat. This is called a *neuralyzer*.'

Suddenly there were six more Men in Black with the nine detectives. The six were wearing dark glasses.

Dee and Kay put on dark glasses.

'What's happening?' asked Janus. 'Who *are* you?'

'A good question,' said Kay. 'In a minute you are going to forget all this.' Then he pushed something on the *neuralyzer*. There was a sudden, strong light, and the detectives could see nothing.

In front of them was a small alien with a human head in its hands.

Dee sat down on the road. 'I'm sorry,' he said to Kay.
'I couldn't . . . kill . . .'

When they could see again, they could remember nothing about Mikey or the *neuralyzer*. They walked quietly back to their cars.

Dee sat down on the road. 'I'm sorry,' he said to Kay. 'I couldn't . . . kill . . .'

Kay looked at Dee. 'This is the last time for Dee,' thought Kay. 'He's tired. We can't use him again.'

'It's OK,' he said. And he aimed his *neuralyzer* at Dee.

Chapter 2   The End of the World

The man ran up and down Madison Avenue.

'The world is finished!' he cried to everybody.

Policeman James Edwards started to walk across to the man, but the man ran away. 'Stop!' called Edwards, and ran after him.

They ran through the New York streets, but the man was too

fast for Edwards. Then a van went past, and Edwards jumped on to the van. He jumped off when the van was near the man, and the two of them fell on to the road together.

Edwards could see the man's eyes, but there was something different about them. *Each eye had two black holes in the centre of it.* Then the man pulled out a gun, but Edwards hit it out of his hand. The gun went flying away and hit the road – and the policeman saw it break into a million pieces.

Suddenly, the man pulled away from Edwards and began to run again. He ran inside a building, and Edwards followed him. There were pictures inside the building and people looking at them. The man ran up the stairs and into a room and Edwards ran after him.

'Stop!' called Edwards.

'You don't understand,' said the man. He was in a corner of the room. 'The world is finished!' And he jumped out of the window.

Edwards watched him fall and heard him hit the street.

♦

'Each eye had two black holes in the centre of it, and his gun broke into a million pieces,' Edwards told his boss.

They were in the police boss's office. He looked at Edwards but did not speak. 'He thinks I'm crazy,' thought Edwards.

His boss got up and went out. A minute later, Laurel Weaver looked in. She was the police doctor. 'I've opened him up,' she said to Edwards. 'Come to my room later, and I can tell you about it.' She turned and went out again.

Suddenly there was a light outside the door, and Edwards shut his eyes. When he opened them again, a man was in the office with him. The man was all in black: black coat, trousers and shoes.

'They were not holes,' said the man.

'What? Who are you?' asked Edwards.

'Call me Kay,' said the man. 'Did he say anything to you?'

'Yes, he said, "The world is finished,"' Edwards told him.

'When?' asked Kay. 'Did he say?'

Edwards looked at him. 'Is *he* crazy, too?' he thought.

'Did you see his gun?' said Kay.

'Yes, I saw it,' said Edwards.

'Let's go to my car,' said Kay. 'We're going to see more guns.'

'Wait a minute,' said Edwards. 'I have papers to write –'

'They're not important,' said Kay. 'Come on.'

Edwards's boss came back into the office. 'Good work, Edwards,' he said, and smiled.

'What's happening?' thought Edwards. He looked at the Man in Black. 'Somebody important,' he thought.

He followed Kay to a black car in the car park. They drove away from the police station. 'Who are you with?' he asked. 'What do you do?'

'We watch the aliens in this world,' said Kay.

'He *is* crazy!' thought Edwards.

They stopped outside a shop. Edwards knew it. 'This is Jeebs's place,' he said. 'Jeeb buys and sells things, but not guns.'

They went inside the small, dirty shop. Jeebs stood behind a table. He had an expensive watch in his hand, and there were more in front of him. He saw Edwards and quickly put the watch down. 'Mr Edwards!' he said.

'Are those yours?' said Edwards, smiling. 'Or are the police looking for those watches, Jeebs?'

'I – I –' began Jeebs.

'But I think you've got something more interesting than watches, Jeebs,' said Edwards. 'Guns!'

'No!' said Jeebs.

'Show him, Jeebs,' said Kay, and he came out of a dark corner of the shop.

'Hello K-Kay,' said Jeebs. 'H-how are you?'

'Show him,' said Kay.

'I don't have any, Kay,' said Jeebs. He was afraid now.

Kay took out a gun. He aimed and fired – and suddenly Jeebs's head wasn't there!

Edwards pulled out his gun. 'You're crazy!' he told Kay. 'Why did you do that? Put down your gun!'

'That was not nice,' somebody said behind him.

Edwards turned quickly and saw Jeebs . . . *with a new head.*

'Show us the guns,' said Kay. Again he aimed his gun at Jeebs, and Jeebs quickly pushed something under the table in front of him. Suddenly, a door opened on the wall behind him.

Edwards saw lines of guns on the wall.

'The man with holes in his eyes,' Kay said to Edwards. 'You saw his gun. Do you see a gun the same as that here?'

'Yes,' said Edwards, and he went across to a gun.

Kay took out a gun. He aimed and fired.

'A *carbonizer*,' said Kay. He turned to Jeebs. 'Did you sell a *carbonizer* to an alien?'

'I . . . I thought he was OK,' said Jeebs.

'A *carbonizer* is a killer's gun,' said Kay. 'The alien wanted to kill somebody. Who?'

'I don't know,' said Jeebs. 'I don't know!'

Kay and Edwards came out of the shop a minute or two later.

'I don't understand any of this,' said Edwards.

'It's OK,' said Kay. 'Now you can forget everything.' He took out his *neuralyzer* and aimed it at Edwards.

Edwards never remembered the strong light in his eyes. All he knew was: one minute he could see a crazy man running along Madison Avenue, and the next minute he was in a Chinese restaurant. He looked across the table and saw a man in black. 'Do I know him?' thought Edwards.

'It's OK,' said Kay. 'Now you can forget everything.' He took out his neuralyzer and aimed it at Edwards.

The man looked at his watch. 'I must go,' he said. He put a piece of paper in front of Edwards. 'You're a clever young man, James,' he said. 'Come and see me tomorrow at 9am.'

He turned and walked out of the restaurant, and Edwards looked at the piece of paper. *James D. Edwards, Saturday, 9am, 504 Battery Road*, he read. He turned the paper over and read: *MiB*.

Chapter 3   A Hole in the Ground

Beatrice worked hard to give her husband a nice hot dinner. But Edgar was never happy with it. There was always something wrong. Tonight it was the meat. 'I don't like this meat!' he said.

Beatrice quietly put a hand on his plate and started to take it away.

'Leave it!' he said. 'Don't take it away. I −'

Suddenly there was a big noise outside. The plates moved on the table. Everything in the house moved.

'Stay there!' said Edgar. He jumped up and opened the door. Then he got his gun and went outside.

Beatrice went to the door and looked out. There was a big hole in the ground. 'Where's your van, Edgar?' she asked.

'I don't know!' cried Edgar. 'It was − Get back in the house!'

Something was in the hole, and Edgar aimed his gun at it.

'*Put the gun on the ground*,' said the thing in the hole.

'Never!' cried Edgar.

Then something long and hairy pulled him into the hole.

Beatrice waited at the dinner table. After about five minutes, she heard Edgar come back into the house.

'What was it?' she asked.

'*Sugar*,' answered Edgar. '*Give me sugar. In water*.'

Beatrice got him a glass of sugar and water and watched him drink it. She was suddenly afraid. 'You − you're different!'

'Sugar, give me sugar. In water.' Beatrice got him a glass of sugar and water.

she said. 'Your face is . . . the same but . . . it's not right . . . '

Edgar put his glass down on the table. He looked at his face in the dark window. Then he pushed some of the face down into his shirt. He turned to Beatrice and smiled. 'Is that better?' he asked.

It was the last thing Beatrice heard before her eyes closed and she fell to the floor.

Chapter 4   A New Job for Edwards

Edwards arrived at 504, Battery Road and followed a man to a room in the building. There were six men in the room. Then a Man in Black came in. 'Sit down,' he told Edwards. 'You're late.'

Edwards sat down. 'Why are we here?' he asked.

'My name is Zed,' the Man in Black said. 'You are all here because you are the best. We want only one man.' He gave them some paper. 'First, there are some questions for you to answer.'

Edwards looked at the paper, then he and the others began to write answers to the questions. They were difficult questions.

After they finished writing, Zed took the men into the next room. There were guns on a table, and across the room was a wall. The wall opened, and Edwards saw a lot of coloured lights. Three moving pictures came out of the lights – two 'aliens' and a 'human'. 'Kill the dangerous thing!' cried Zed.

The six men fired at the aliens, but Edwards aimed and fired at the human – a little girl.

'Why the girl?' Zed asked him.

'The aliens aren't dangerous,' said Edwards. 'One of them can't think because it doesn't have a head. First, I thought that the other alien was dangerous, but when I looked more carefully I saw that it had a smile on its face. But for the girl it wasn't a game. She wanted to kill.'

Zed went out of the room and spoke to another Man in Black. Edwards saw the other man through the open door. It was the man from the Chinese restaurant.

'Very good,' Zed told everybody when he came back into the room. 'Now follow me.'

Edwards was the last to leave the room. The man from the Chinese restaurant walked across to him.

'What's happening?' asked Edwards. 'Who are you people?'

'Come with me,' said the man. 'Call me Kay.'

He took Edwards away from the six other men. They got to a corner and turned to look at the others. They saw Zed aim a *neuralyzer* at the six, and there was a sudden white light. After that, Zed took them away.

'Who are you?' Edwards asked Kay again.

'Our job is to find and talk with aliens,' said Kay. 'We started to see them in the early 1950s, and the Men in Black started in 1955. Then some aliens talked to us on March 2, 1961, near New York City. "We have no home," they told us. "Can we come and live on earth?" "OK," we said. "But be friendly." We didn't tell anybody. Look at this photograph of the 1964 World's Fair.' He showed Edwards a photograph. 'You see those two tall buildings? They each have a space ship on them. People didn't know that they were *real* space ships.' He looked at Edwards. 'Now aliens arrive here every year, but nobody knows about them.'

'Well, thanks for an interesting morning,' said Edwards. 'Can you take me out of here now?' 'The man is crazy,' he thought.

'I want a cup of coffee first,' said Kay, and opened a door. In

'Hello' Kay said to the aliens. 'How are you?' The aliens cried out their answers. Kay got a cup of coffee.

12

the next room were four small aliens. Edwards heard them speaking a different language – *and he knew that they were not from this Earth*. His mouth fell open.

'Hello,' Kay said to the aliens. 'How are you?'

The aliens cried out their answers.

Kay got a cup of coffee. 'There are usually fifteen hundred aliens on Earth at any one time,' Kay told Edwards. 'Most of them are here in New York. They try to be same as us when they're here. Some are better than others. Most are friendly and work hard.' He smiled. 'Humans are happy not to know about them.'

Slowly, Edwards began to understand. 'You – you want me to be a Man in Black,' he said.

'That's right,' said Kay. 'You're the best of the best. But you'll lose your name, and nobody will know you, not your family, not your friends – nobody.' He finished his coffee. 'Think about it, and give me your answer tomorrow morning.'

Chapter 5   The Bug Van

Edgar did not go to bed that night. He sat at the table and moved his head up and down, down and up. 'I must get it right,' he thought. 'It hurts to move it, but I can't live with humans without a head.'

Early the next morning, a van arrived. It stopped outside the garage. Edgar went to look. There was a picture of a big bug on the van. A man got out.

Edgar smiled. 'It's a nice big van,' he thought. He walked across to the garage, and the man turned to look at him.

'Hello, Edgar,' the man said. 'I've come to kill those bugs in the garage. You remember? Hundreds of them. You asked me to –'

Edgar moved quickly. He killed the man, then got into the van and drove it across to the hole in the ground. He opened the van's back doors, and jumped down into the hole.

The space ship was cold now. Edgar pushed it up out of the hole, and into the back of the van. He smiled. 'That was easy,' he said. Then he climbed into the van and drove away.

Chapter 6   A Baby Alien

'You want me to be a Man in Black? Well, OK, I will,' Edwards told Kay.

'Good, come with me,' said Kay.

They went into a big room, and Edwards saw humans and aliens at work together. He saw Zed in front of a big screen with a picture of the world. There were thousands of small lights all over the picture.

'This picture shows every alien in the world at any one time,' Kay told Edwards. 'Every light on that screen is an alien.'

They went with Zed into another room and Zed gave Edwards a black coat, black trousers and black shoes. 'Put them on,' he said. 'From now on your name is James Darrel Edwards, but you're going to take the name "Jay".'

They went to Zed's office.

'We have a Manhattan alien out on the New Jersey road,' Zed told Kay. 'What's he doing there?'

'Who is it?' asked Kay.

'Redgick,' answered Zed. 'Go and take him. Take Jay with you.'

Jay followed Kay outside and got into a black Ford car. It was a 1986 Ford, but when they moved off, they moved faster than any Ford that Jay knew.

They found the car on the New Jersey Road. There was a man about thirty years old in the front, and a woman in the back. 'She's going to have a baby soon,' thought Jay.

'Papers, please,' Kay said to the driver. The driver gave him

The space ship was cold now. Edgar pushed it up out of the hole.

some papers. Kay looked at them then gave them back. 'Now your *other* papers, please, Mr Redgick,' Kay said.

The man looked at him for a minute, then took two more papers from his coat. The word *Alien* was on each of the papers, and photographs of an alien husband and wife. Their faces were the same as fish faces – long and thin. But he thought they were friendly.

Jay looked at Mr Redgick and his wife again. They were the same as any human husband and wife to him.

Kay gave the papers back to the driver. 'Where are you going?' he said. 'Your papers are for Manhattan only.'

'It's my wife,' said Mr Redgick. 'She's going to have a baby.'

'How soon?' asked Kay.

The woman cried, 'Aagh!' and closed her eyes. It was an answer to Kay's question: *very* soon.

'OK,' said Kay. He turned to Jay. 'You do it.'

'Me?' said Jay. 'But I –'

'It's easy,' said Kay.

So, Jay got into the back of the car with Mrs Redgick. He was afraid, and it showed on his face. Mr Redgick looked at Jay, then said, 'Does he know –?'

'Yes,' said Kay. 'He does this all the time. Come on, Redgick. I want to ask you one or two things.' He took Mr Redgick three or four metres away from the car. 'The doctor lives on Sixty-fourth Street. But this road goes *out* of town. Why are you out here?'

Redgick looked at the ground. 'We – we're going to meet somebody.'

'Who?' asked Kay.

'Well – it's a ship,' answered Redgick.

'No ship is leaving today,' said Kay. 'And why do you want to leave here? What's suddenly wrong with our world?'

'There are new aliens arriving, and we – we don't like some of them,' said Redgick.

'Quick!' called Jay from the car. 'Come here!'

Kay moved across to the car, and Jay came out quickly. There was an alien baby in his arms. 'I've done it!' Jay said. 'Mr Redgick, you're a father!'

Mr Redgick ran to see his wife. She was OK, and after two or three minutes, Kay told them, 'You can go.' The Redgicks drove away, and Kay and Jay went back to their car.

'Redgick is afraid of something,' said Kay. 'He was ready to take a new baby out of here on a space ship today. Why?'

They drove back into the city. Kay stopped near a newspaper shop. He came back with a newspaper and showed Jay the front of it: *Farm Wife says 'Alien Took My Husband's Body!'*

♦

Beatrice came out of the house to meet them. 'Can I help you?' she asked. 'My name's Beatrice.'

Kay looked at the big hole in the ground near the house.

'Are you here to laugh at me, too?' asked Beatrice. 'The other policemen laughed at my story.'

'We're not here to laugh,' said Kay. 'Is it OK to come in?'

They went into the house and sat down. Beatrice gave them a cold drink, then began to tell her story.

'Edgar came in from work,' she said. 'He was tired. We started to eat dinner, and then we heard this big noise. Edgar got his gun and went outside. There was a big hole in the ground. When Edgar came back, he was ... different. It wasn't Edgar. It was somebody *wearing* him. Wearing his body!'

'Did he say anything?' asked Kay.

'He asked for water,' Beatrice remembered. 'Sugar water.'

'Sugar water,' said Kay.

He looked at Jay, then took out his *neuralyzer*. Jay and Kay put on dark glasses, and Kay aimed the *neuralyzer* at Beatrice. After the light, he said, 'OK, Beatrice, there was no alien. And Edgar ran away with an old girlfriend. Remember that, and go and stay

17

There was an alien baby in Jay's arms. 'I've done it!'
Jay said. 'Mr Redgick, you're a father!'

Kay and Jay went into the house and sat down. Beatrice gave them a cold drink, then began to tell her story.

with your mother for a week. I want you to think: "Everything is going to be better without Edgar."'

He went out to the hole again, and Jay followed him. Kay took a small box from his coat and moved it across the hole. A green light came on in the box. 'Oh, no!' he said. 'It was a Bug.'

'Is that bad?' said Jay.

'Bugs kill things – aliens and people,' said Kay. 'And we have the Bug in town. Yes, that's bad.'

Chapter 7   Bugs in the Restaurant

Rosenberg looked at his watch. He did not want to be late. Not for something as important as this. He put on his coat and hat, took his cat under one arm, and a box under the other. He shut the shop. It was nearly dark outside, and he walked quickly along the grey streets. 'What's that?' he thought. 'Something is behind me!' He looked back, but it was only a van.

He got to the Russian restaurant and went inside. The Arquillian alien was there. He stood up and Rosenberg put the box down on the table between them. The cat sat quietly on the box.

The Arquillian gave Rosenberg a drink, and they both drank.

A man came over to their table – and suddenly there were Bugs all over it. Rosenberg looked up at the man. 'I know him. Where did I see him before?' he thought. And then he remembered. 'The newspaper! The photograph of the farmer called Edgar.'

The Arquillian looked at the man – and knew him, too.

'You can kill us,' Rosenberg told Edgar, 'but you can't make the Baltians and Arquillians fight over the Third Galaxy. You can't start the fighting.'

Edgar smiled. Then he killed the Arquillian and Rosenberg, and pushed the cat off the box. He put the box under his arm, and ran out of the restaurant.

Chapter 8   The Little Green Man

Dr Laurel Weaver looked at the second body from the Russian restaurant. The cat sat on a bed near her and watched her cut into it with her knife. Nothing inside the body was human.

'Very interesting,' she began.

'What is it?' said somebody behind her.

She turned quickly and saw two men.

Kay said, 'I'm Doctor Leo Menville. This is Doctor White. Have you got something unusual there?'

*The cat sat on a bed near Dr Laurel Weaver and watched
her cut into the body with a knife.*

'Yes,' said Laurel.

Kay moved nearer and looked at the body.

'Is that your cat?' Jay asked Laurel.

'It is now,' said Laurel. 'It came in with the bodies.' She looked carefully at him. 'Do I know you?'

'I wanted to ask you the same thing,' said Jay.

Laurel asked Jay to put his hand inside the body.

'I think,' she said quietly to Jay, 'something *used* this body and moved around in it. But what?'

Jay looked at Dr Weaver. 'She's clever *and* beautiful,' he thought.

'What do you think?' Kay asked Jay.

'*Very* interesting,' answered Jay, and he looked at Laurel.

'What do you think of the *body*?' said Kay.

'What? Oh, I don't know,' said Jay.

'Look,' said Laurel. She put a finger near the dead man's ear. There was a thin line behind it.

Jay put out a hand and pushed the ear. There was a noise, *and then the dead man's face opened like a door*. Inside the head was a small room, with TV screens. A little green man sat in front of one of the screens. Jay and Laurel looked at the little green man, and their mouths fell open.

The little man tried to say something. '*To stop . . . fighting . . . galaxy . . . on Orion's be . . . be . . .*'

'Belt?' asked Jay.

'*Yes . . . belt . . .*' said the green man. Then he fell down.

'Galaxy? Fighting?' said Jay. He looked at Kay. 'What −?'

'The Baltians and Arquillians are two galaxies,' Kay told him. 'They're fighting over the Third Galaxy − they fight again and again, year after year.'

Laurel looked at Jay and Kay. 'You're not doctors,' she said.

'No,' said Jay. He looked at Kay. 'Is he dead?'

'Yes,' said Kay. 'His name was Rosenberg.'

Laurel asked Jay to put his hand inside the body. 'I think,'
she said quietly to Jay, 'something used this body and
moved around in it. But what?'

'You knew the little green man?' asked Jay.

'Yes,' said Kay. 'And I liked him.'

'I was right!' cried Laurel. 'This is an alien, not a human! I –'

Before she could finish, Kay took out his *neuralyzer* . . .'

♦

Edgar sat in the back of the van, next to Rosenberg's box. He had Rosenberg's box in his hands. He could not get it open, and he was angry. He threw it at the van doors, and it broke open. He laughed and looked inside – and stopped laughing. There was nothing in the box.

'No!' he cried. 'No, no, no!'

♦

Jay was tired. It was early in the morning and he and Kay were in the MiB office. The big screen showed a picture of Orion. Seven or eight other men watched the screen with Jay and Kay.

'This is Orion,' said Zed. 'Those three stars are Orion's Belt. There are no galaxies on Orion's Belt. Galaxies are made of billions of stars. I don't think the man said "Belt". You heard wrong, Jay.'

Kay looked at the screen. There were not as many lights on the world as earlier. 'All over the world, they're leaving,' he said.

'Redgick was the first,' said Zed. 'Twelve went in the last hour.'

'What do they know . . . and what *don't* we know?' asked Jay.

Kay asked for another picture, and this time it was a picture of the world in space. He moved nearer to the screen. 'That's an Arquillian space ship,' he said, and put his finger on the screen.

'And we've got a dead Arquillian,' said Zed. 'Kay, get down to Rosenberg's shop. Look around – but be careful. And take guns.'

Kay took Jay to a room and opened a box. He took out a big gun. Jay smiled and waited to get one the same. But Kay gave him the smallest gun in the box. 'We call it the Noisy Bird,' said Kay.

'You get a big gun, and I get a Noisy Bird?' said Jay.

Kay did not answer. He went out to the car.

♦

Edgar broke the window of Rosenberg's shop. Nobody heard him. It was dark, and there was nobody in the street. He climbed inside and began to move round. He was angry, and he started to break things. There were pictures of cats on the wall, but where –?

Edgar heard the sound of a truck outside. He looked out and saw his van up on the back of a big city police truck. Edgar ran out and across the street.

'Hey! That's my van!' he said to the truck driver.

'Remember to tell them that at the police station when you ask for it back,' said the driver. 'You can't leave a van here.'

Edgar killed the truck driver without a word.

Chapter 9 Conversation with a Dog

'Somebody was here before us,' said Jay. 'And he was angry.' Jay walked across pieces of glass to the wall. Pictures of a cat. Lots of them. Near them were some cats' collars. Jay took a collar in his hand and looked at it. 'Rosenberg loved his cats,' he said.

Through the window, Jay saw a big man with a gun in each hand. He suddenly remembered a picture in Edgar's house. 'Kay, get down!' he cried.

Jay pulled out his Noisy Bird and fired at Edgar. He did not hit him, but the gun made a big noise. Edgar turned and ran down the street.

'The Bug is in Edgar's body!' said Jay. 'That was him!'

He ran after Edgar, and Kay followed. They got to the street and saw Edgar drive away in the police truck, with the van up behind it. Jay ran into the road and fired his Noisy Bird again. He hit something at the back of the truck, and the van fell off.

The police truck turned a corner and Jay and Kay walked across to the van. Kay looked inside the van and smiled.

'That Bug is not leaving town,' he said. 'We've got his space ship here.'

Kay found a street telephone and phoned Zed. 'What's happening now?' he asked.

'Aliens are leaving every five or ten minutes,' Zed told him. 'And there's more bad news.'

Kay listened for a minute, then put the phone down. 'There's a Baltian space ship out there now, ready to fight,' he told Jay.

'The little green man's family?' said Jay.

'That's right,' said Kay. 'We need help.'

They drove across town. 'The Bugs are happy when the Baltians and Arquillians fight,' Kay told Jay. 'Sometimes the two galaxies stop fighting. How can the Bugs start them fighting again? Answer: By getting their hands on the Third Galaxy.'

They stopped in front of a shop. Inside, a man in an old coat and hat looked up when they came in. Near him was a small white dog with big round eyes. Jay waited for Kay to speak to the man – but he spoke to the dog!

'Hello, Frank,' said Kay.

'Sorry, Kay,' said the dog. 'I can't talk now. My ship's leaving.'

Kay pulled the dog across to him. 'Arquillians and Baltians,' he said. 'What do you know about them? What's the story?'

'They're fighting about the Third Galaxy,' said Frank. 'Or they were. Then the Baltians said to the Arquillians, "OK, we're going to give you the Third Galaxy", but the Bugs had other plans. They don't want the fighting between the Baltians and Arquillians to stop.'

'Ask about the Belt,' Jay said to Kay. He could not talk to a *dog!*

*Kay pulled the dog across to him. 'Arquillians and Baltians,'
he said. 'What do you know about them?
What's the story?'*

'I don't understand it,' answered the dog. 'They say the galaxy is here, on Earth.'

'Here?' said Jay. 'Millions of stars? On Earth? How?'

'A galaxy can be very small,' said the dog. 'As small as a penny or a jewel for example. Now, I must go. Please, Kay.'

'OK,' said Kay. And the dog got its bag and ran out of the shop.

'I thought the little green man tried to say "Belt,"' said Jay. 'But his English wasn't very good. Think of the words for "belt" in other languages. What could be the same as a belt to an alien?' Suddenly, Jay knew. 'We must see Dr Laurel Weaver!' he said. 'Quickly!'

◆

The cat jumped on to Dr Weaver's desk. Laurel smiled at it. It was a friendly cat. She looked at its collar − and at the jewel on the collar. There was a word on the jewel: *Orion*.

'Orion,' Laurel said to the cat. 'That's a pretty name.'

The jewel was very beautiful. She looked into it − and saw millions of stars, all of different colours.

Suddenly, she heard feet outside her door. People running. Orion made an angry noise and jumped off the desk.

◆

Kay drove fast. 'We must get the Third Galaxy before the Bug does,' he told Jay.

'We aren't looking for a belt in the sky,' said Jay. 'We're looking for something that is nearly the same as a real belt. I think it's the collar on Rosenberg's cat!'

The car stopped outside Dr Weaver's office.

'I can do this,' said Jay. 'You wait here for two minutes.'

'Why?' asked Kay.

'Because I can get the cat,' said Jay. 'You don't have to use your *neuralyzer* on anybody.'

'OK,' said Kay. 'Two minutes.'

♦

Edgar stood in front of Dr Weaver. 'I don't know this man,' she thought, 'but something tells me he's dangerous.'

'The cat. Where is it?' he said. 'Tell me!'

'I don't know,' she said. 'It ran under those boxes, over there.'

'Get it!' the man told her. He pulled her across the room to the boxes. Dr Weaver put her hand down behind them, and Orion ran out and jumped on to a tall cupboard.

The man started to move across to Orion, then he stopped. Somebody was outside.

'Hello?' said Jay from outside. 'Anybody there?'

The man looked at Dr Weaver. 'Don't say anything,' he told her quietly. Then he got under a table.

A minute later, Jay walked into the room. 'Hello,' he said. He smiled at Laurel. 'They brought a cat in here the other day. Did it say "Orion" on the collar?'

'Yes,' said Laurel. 'That's right.'

'I want to take that cat with me,' said Jay. 'Where is it?'

'I – I don't know,' said Laurel. Then she said quietly, 'Perhaps you could take *me* with you. Now.'

'Take you?' he said. He smiled. 'Well –'

Suddenly the table between them jumped up, and the man under it pulled Dr Weaver across in front of him and aimed his gun at her head.

Jay looked at him. It was Edgar. The Bug.

Chapter 10   Guns and Space Ships

The door opened fast and Kay ran in. He aimed his gun at the Bug. 'Take your hands off her!' he said.

'Shut up, boy,' Edgar said. He aimed his gun at Laurel's head.

Edgar aimed his gun at Laurel's head.

Suddenly something flew across the room. It was Orion! The cat fell on Edgar, and Edgar put out a hand and caught the animal. Then he saw the jewel on Orion's collar.

Jay saw it, too. The Third Galaxy was *inside* that jewel!

Edgar took the jewel and quickly put it into his mouth and ate it. Then he pushed his gun back into Laurel's face. Jay and Kay moved away from him. 'That's better,' said Edgar. 'Now put down your guns.'

Jay put down his gun, but Kay did not move.

'You can't get far without your ship,' Kay told the Bug.

'Put the gun down!' said Edgar.

'Never,' said Kay.

Edgar began to move away.

'It's OK, Laurel,' said Jay.

'*How* is it OK?' she asked, afraid.

'It's *going* to be OK,' said Jay.

But suddenly the Bug jumped back and out through the window with Laurel. Kay and Jay ran outside, but they were too late. Edgar pulled a taxi driver from his taxi, and pushed Laurel into it.

'Drive!' he told her.

Jay started running after the taxi, but he was too slow.

'Come on!' cried Kay. 'He's not getting off this world in a taxi.'

Jay ran back to Kay, and they got into their car.

They drove to the MiB office, but Edgar was not there. His space ship was there, but everything was quiet.

'Perhaps he's not going to come here,' said Jay.

'He must,' said Kay.

Then a noise came from the big screen and they went across. Zed was there. On the screen, everybody could see the Baltian space ship and the Arquillian space ship.

'The Arquillians want the Third Galaxy,' said Kay. 'But the Baltians don't have it.'

'That's right,' said Zed. 'And all of them are angry.'

Suddenly a thin red line came from the Arquillian ship. To get to the Baltian ship, it ran through the Earth.

'The Arquillians are firing at the Baltians through the North Sea,' said Zed.

Next, the Baltians fired a red line back to the Arquillians. Again, it went through the Earth.

'Now they must talk again,' Zed told Jay. 'They can each fire one, then they must talk.'

'How much talking must they do before they start firing again?' asked Jay. He was afraid.

'They talk for one hour,' said Kay. He turned to Zed. 'Where are all the space ships?'

'All gone,' said Zed.

'All of them?' said Kay.

'Frank the Dog took the last ship on Earth,' said Zed.

There was a picture of the 1964 World's Fair above the screen. Jay looked at the two space ships on the tall buildings in the picture. 'Do they – ?' he began.

Kay and Zed looked at him, then looked at the picture and smiled.

'You're right! Come on!' Kay said to Jay. They ran out to their car and drove fast to the two World's Fair buildings.

♦

'He's got Laurel!' cried Jay.

He and Kay looked up. They saw Edgar, with Dr Weaver under his arm. They saw him climb one of the tall buildings. Then they watched him walk across to the space ship. He pushed Laurel in front of him. But suddenly she turned and kicked him in the face! He fell back – and she jumped off the building.

Jay watched her. 'No!' he cried. Then he saw Laurel fall into a tree. She hit it hard, but it stopped her.

'She's OK,' said Kay. 'Come on.'

They opened the back of the car and pulled out some guns. Then Kay got a long black box and opened it. He pulled out a big gun – a very big gun!

'How do you fire that?' said Jay. 'Do you know?'

They heard a noise and looked up. Edgar was inside the space ship. It began to turn round and round . . . faster and faster . . . then it began to move up into the sky . . .

Kay aimed the big gun at the space ship. Jay aimed his gun. They fired. There was no noise, but Jay saw Edgar's ship stop, and begin to come back down to Earth. 'Something is pulling it back!' he thought. 'These guns . . . they're pulling the space ship back to Earth!'

The ship hit the ground with a BANG! A minute later,

Kay aimed his gun at the Bug. 'Put your hands on your head.' Edgar
laughed, and put his hands above his head.

the door of the ship opened, and Edgar climbed out.

Kay aimed his gun at the Bug. 'Put your hands on your head.'

Edgar laughed, and put his hands above his head. Suddenly, they saw Edgar's body open. *And a Bug bigger than a truck climbed out.* Jay saw that he wore the jewel of the Third Galaxy on his front.

He and Kay aimed their guns at the Bug. But the Bug opened

his mouth, and out came something brown and wet, and it pulled their guns out of their hands. The Bug ate the guns, then hit Jay and Kay five metres across the street.

They stood up and saw the Bug run to the tall building.

'He wants to get away in the other space ship!' said Jay.

Kay began to run after the Bug.

'What are you doing?' asked Jay, and followed him.

'I'm going to get my gun back,' said Kay.

'What?' cried Jay.

'Bug!' called Kay. 'Listen to me, Bug! I'm talking to you! How many of you do I hit and kill with a newspaper, do you know? Hundreds? Thousands? You're nothing, Bug!'

The Bug stopped and turned round. He was angry. Then he opened his mouth, moved back to Kay – and ate him.

Chapter 11   Inside the Bug

'Kay –!' cried Jay. He watched the Bug eat Kay. 'No!'

But then he saw something moving inside the Bug! 'Kay's not dead!' he thought. 'He's moving inside the Bug! He's trying to get the guns! I must do something to stop the Bug. He must not get on that space ship.'

Jay ran after the Bug. 'Are you afraid of me?' he cried. 'Turn and fight! Come on! Perhaps you're a big Bug in your world, but this is New York City. You're nothing here!'

The Bug turned and hit Jay hard. The young man flew six metres through the sky and fell into the back of an old truck. When he opened his eyes, Jaw saw something in one corner of the truck – thousands of little bugs – *earth* bugs, not aliens. He smiled and kicked open the back of the truck – and out fell the thousands of bugs. Jay jumped down to the ground after them.

'Hey, Bug!' he called. 'Look!'

The Bug stopped and turned round. He saw the thousands of earth bugs on the ground under Jay's feet.

'Are they your brothers and sisters?' said Jay, and he laughed. Then he jumped down on them, hard – SCRUNCH! 'Who was that? What do you think?' His foot came down again. SCRUNCH! 'Was that your brother Bob?' SCRUNCH! 'And your sister Belle?'

The Bug did not like it. He was angry. He began to climb back down the tall building.

Jay walked across to him. SCRUNCH! SCRUNCH! SCRUNCH! All the time, he watched the front of the Bug. He could see Kay moving inside with one of the guns now.

'Goodbye, Edgar,' he said quietly.

And then suddenly there was a big noise – BANG! – and Edgar the Bug was suddenly all over the street in hundreds of little pieces.

And there was Kay, with the gun in his hand.

♦

You *wanted* Edgar to eat you,' said Jay, some minutes later.

Kay smiled, and used his phone to call Zed. When Zed answered, he said, 'We have the Third Galaxy. Tell the Arquillians.'

Suddenly there was a noise behind them. They turned. It was the Bug! One big piece of him was not dead. It moved slowly across to them! Then there was a BANG! And the big piece of the Bug flew into a million little pieces.

Jay and Kay turned round and saw Dr Weaver behind them. She had the big gun in her hand.

'You boys have an interesting job,' she said.

'She saw everything from the tree,' thought Jay. He was not happy about that. 'Now Kay will use the *neuralyzer* on her.'

The three of them drove back to the MiB building and stopped outside. Dr Weaver waited in the car, and Jay talked

Elle was all in black now. She was not Laurel Weaver - she was Elle.

ACTIVITIES

Chapters 1–4

Before you read

1 Look at the picture on page 8.
  a Who is in the picture?
  b What are they wearing?
  c What do you think is happening?

2 Find these words in your dictionary. They are all in the story.
  aim   hole   piece   real
  Now use the words in these sentences.
  a The man ..... at the bird. He wanted to kill it.
  b The car stopped because there was a big ..... in the middle of
     the road.
  c The glass fell onto the floor and broke into small ......
  d The flowers on the table weren't ..... – they were paper flowers.

3 Find these words in your dictionary.
  a human/alien
  b fire/ground
  Now use the words to make two sentences.

After you read

4 In Chapters 1–4, who:
  a are the men in the back of Nick's van?
  b has a human head in its hands?
  c watches a man jump out of a window, and hears him hit the
     street?
  d sells a carbonizer to an alien?
  e works hard to give her husband a nice dinner?

5 Do you think that there really are aliens? Why/why not?

Chapters 5–8

Before you read

6 Will Edwards answer 'yes' or 'no'? Do you think he wants to be a
   Man in Black? Why/why not?

7 Find these words in your dictionary. Then answer the questions about them.

body   bug

   a Do people usually like or hate bugs? Are they dangerous? What do bugs do to people?

   b When a man or a woman dies, what usually happens to his/her body?

After you read

8 Who says these words? Who to?

   a 'You want me to be a Man in Black? Well OK, I will.'

   b 'Bugs kill things – aliens and people.'

   c 'You can't start the fighting.'

   d 'You knew the little green man?'

9 Answer these questions.

   a What do the thousands of small lights on Zed's screen show?

   b What car does Kay drive?

   c What are the Redgicks' faces the same as?

   d Where does Rosenberg meet the Arquillian?

   e What happens when Jay pushes the dead man's ear?

Chapters 9–12

Before you read

10 Look at the pictures on pages 30, 33 and 36.
   What do you think will happen to:

   a Edgar

   b Laurel

11 Find the word *jewel* in your dictionary. Then look at the picture on page 21. What do you think is inside the jewel on the cat's neck?

After you read

12 Are these sentences right or wrong?

   a The Bugs want the Baltians and Arquillians to fight.

   b Frank is a small white cat with big round eyes.

   c The Third Galaxy is inside the cat's jewel.

d Edgar gets into the space ship on the tall building.

e The bug opens his mouth and eats Laurel.

13 Work with another student. Have a conversation.

Student A: You are Kay. You were inside the Bug. What did you see? How did you feel? Tell Student B.

Student B: You are Jay. Ask Student A questions about the inside of the Bug.

Writing

14 In the story, who do you like most? Why? Who don't you like? Why?

15 You work for the *New York Times*. Write a newspaper story about Beatrice and Edgar. Begin with these words: *Farm Wife says 'Alien Took My Husband's Body!'*

16 At the end of the story a woman, Elle, begins to work with the Men in Black. You are Jay. Write about Elle for Zed. Do you think she will do the job in a different way because she is a woman?

17 It is a year after the story ends. You are Kay. You can't remember your old life and what happened to you inside the Bug. Write a letter to Jay about your new life. Tell him where you live, what you are doing, and how you feel.

Answers for the activities in this book are available from your local
Pearson Education office or contact: Penguin Readers Marketing Department,
Pearson Education, Edinburgh Gate, Harlow, Essex, CM20 2JE.